The path to the wise man

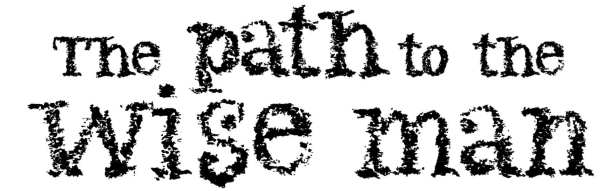

SALARIYA
BH
BOOK HOUSE

Principle 1

Chi ghts

2

It was very rare to see anyone on the rocky path that climbed up the horn-shaped mountain to the Temple of the Oracle. But one day, three children from different villages all set off on the same path. They all wanted to achieve the same goal: to receive the knowledge of the wisest man.

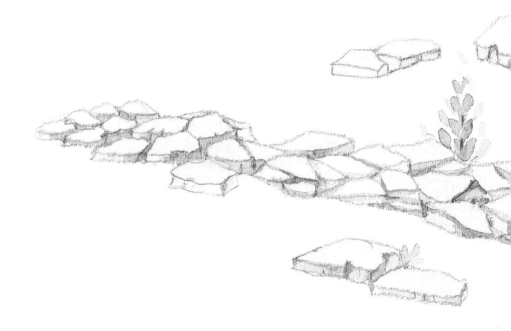

The chiefs of each village were already very old, and somebody would soon have to take over from them. So they had each chosen the cleverest young person in the village to receive the knowledge from the Oracle. Each child not only had to stand out from the others, but also had to surprise the wise man.

The inhabitants of Windhaven were real masters
at making glass. Their child, Narcissus, was chosen
for his cleverness. With little mirrors and lenses
sewn into his clothes and glass filigrees on his hat
and back, he would surely dazzle the Oracle and be
the Chosen One.

In the cotton fields of the south, the inhabitants of Threadweavery had chosen Magnolia, convinced that she would fascinate the wise man with her beauty. And, as they were so skilful with their needles and thread, they had woven and sewn layers and layers of fine cloth to make the most elegant of dresses for her.

Amid the leafy forests of Woodmansville,
the villagers had chosen Thor, and decided to
transform him into the living image of strength
and bravery. As the expert carpenters that
they were, they had felled a hundred-year-old
oak tree to make the boy's armour, helmet
and shield.

The three children made their way up
the narrow, rocky path in silence.
'I'm the strongest,' said Thor to himself.
'I'm the most beautiful,' thought Magnolia.
'I'm much cleverer than the others,'
said Narcissus.
But which one of them would impress
the Oracle most?

14

Halfway up the path, the three adventurers came to
a gully with a torrential river below.
They glanced quickly at each other, without saying
a word, each one frantically thinking of a way to
overcome this obstacle to continue the journey.

'I'll make a parachute to get me to the other side,'
thought Magnolia. She took some of the cotton and
silk layers from her dress and began to sew. But
she was none too sure that her plan would work.
'What if there isn't enough wind and I fall into
the gully?'

Narcissus made binoculars with some of his glass lenses, convinced that they would help him to see a path to cross the gully. He used one of the lenses to light a fire, too. 'Somebody may see the smoke and come to help me,' he said to himself.

Meanwhile, Thor had taken off his armour to build a small raft that would help him to cross the river; but he was worried that the current might be strong enough to drag him away.

None of them had noticed that the hot air
from the fire was inflating the parachute.
'It will blow away!' Magnolia shouted.
Thor quickly tied his raft onto it to weigh it
down, but it started rising.
'Quick, let's all jump on!' said Narcissus.

24

The children couldn't stop laughing as they sped along on their hot-air balloon. They were amazed that it could carry all three of them along through the clouds. Why had they all mistrusted each other so much? They realised now that it was much more fun and less tiresome to travel together.

Thor, Magnolia and Narcissus flew almost to
the entrance of the Temple of the Oracle.
When they saw the Oracle sitting next to a
fountain, they remembered that they no longer
had any armour, beautiful costumes or mirrors
to impress the Master.

'Now, what will I see in each of you when I choose my disciple?' the Oracle asked all three of them.
'I won't see anything, because I'm blind,' said the wise man, and he began to laugh.
'But my heart can see further than my eyes, and it tells me that the three of you deserve to be here, because you have learnt the first lesson.'

It was true! They had learnt that they could make better progress by working together as a team. Trying to impress others just gets in the way. Then the Oracle opened the temple doors so they could start their never-ending journey to wisdom.

Principle 1

of Children's Rights:

A child should enjoy all the rights stated in this Declaration. These rights must apply to all children, without any kind of exception or discrimination because of race, colour, gender, language, religion, political opinion, national and social origins, economic position, whether by birth or other condition, either of the child or the child's family.

In the same way that the wise man in the story opens the doors of knowledge to all three children, the Rights of the Child do not make any kind of discrimination between the young people of the Earth, whatever their culture, way of thinking or appearance.

Furthermore, the story considers cultural diversity as a source of enrichment for all, rather than a source of confrontation.

Children's Rights

Adopted by the General Assembly of the United Nations in Resolution 1386 (XIV) of 10 December 1959.

PREAMBLE

I. *Whereas* the peoples of the United Nations have, in the Charter, reaffirmed their faith in fundamental human rights and in the dignity and worth of the human person, and have determined to promote social progress and better standards of life in larger freedom,

II. *Whereas* the United Nations has, in the Universal Declaration of Human Rights, proclaimed that everyone is entitled to all the rights and freedoms set forth therein, without distinction of any kind, such as race, colour, sex, language, religion, political or other opinion, national or social origin, property, birth or other status,

III. *Whereas* the child, by reason of his physical and mental immaturity, needs special safeguards and care, including appropriate legal protection, before as well as after birth,

IV. *Whereas* the need for such special safeguards has been stated in the Geneva Declaration of the Rights of the Child of 1924, and recognised in the Universal Declaration of Human Rights and in the statutes of specialised agencies and international organisations concerned with the welfare of children,

V. *Whereas* mankind owes to the child the best it has to give,

VI. Now, therefore, *The General Assembly* proclaims this Declaration of the Rights of the Child to the end that he may have a happy childhood and enjoy for his own good and for the good of society the rights and freedoms herein set forth, and calls upon parents, upon men and women as individuals. And upon voluntary organisations, local authorities and national Governments to recognise these rights and strive for their observance by legislative and other measures progressively taken in accordance with the following principles:

Principle 1
The child shall enjoy all the rights set forth in this Declaration. Every child, without any exception whatsoever, shall be entitled to these rights, without distinction or discrimination on account of race, colour, sex, language, religion, political or other opinion, national or social origin, property, birth or other status, whether of himself or of his family.

Principle 2
The child shall enjoy special protection, and shall be given opportunities and facilities, by law and by other means, to enable him to develop physically, mentally, morally, spiritually and socially in a healthy and normal manner and in conditions of freedom and dignity. In the enactment of laws for this purpose, the best interests of the child shall be the paramount consideration.

Principle 3
The child shall be entitled from his birth to a name and a nationality.

Principle 4
The child shall enjoy the benefits of social security. He shall be entitled to grow and develop in health; to this end, special care and protection shall be provided both to him and to his mother, including adequate pre-natal and post-natal care.

The child shall have the right to adequate nutrition, housing, recreation and medical services.

Principle 5
The child who is physically, mentally or socially handicapped shall be given the special treatment, education and care required by his particular condition.

Principle 6
The child, for the full and harmonious development of his personality, needs love and understanding. He shall, wherever possible, grow up in the care and under the responsibility of his parents, and, in any case, in an atmosphere of affection and of moral and material security; a child of tender years shall not, save in exceptional circumstances, be separated from his mother. Society and the public authorities shall have the duty to extend particular care to children without a family and to those without adequate means of support. Payment of State and other assistance towards the maintenance of children of large families is desirable.

Principle 7
The child is entitled to receive education, which shall be free and compulsory, at least in the elementary stages. He shall be given an education which will promote his general culture, and enable him, on a basis of equal opportunity, to develop his abilities, his individual judgement, and his sense of moral and social responsibility, and to become a useful member of society.

The best interests of the child shall be the guiding principle of those responsible for his education and guidance; that responsibility lies in the first place with his parents.

The child shall have full opportunity for play and recreation, which should be directed to the same purposes as education; society and the public authorities shall endeavour to promote the enjoyment of this right.

Principle 8
The child shall in all circumstances be among the first to receive protection and relief.

Principle 9
The child shall be protected against all forms of neglect, cruelty and exploitation. He shall not be the subject of traffic, in any form.

The child shall not be admitted to employment before an appropriate minimum age; he shall in no case be caused or permitted to engage in any occupation or employment which would prejudice his health or education, or interfere with his physical, mental or moral development.

Principle 10
The child shall be protected from practices which may foster racial, religious and any other form of discrimination. He shall be brought up in a spirit of understanding, tolerance, friendship among peoples, peace and universal brotherhood, and in full consciousness that his energy and talents should be devoted to the service of his fellow men.

Visit our **new** online shop at
shop.salariya.com
for great offers, gift ideas, all our new
releases and free postage and packaging.

Published in Great Britain in MMXIII by
Book House, an imprint of
The Salariya Book Company Ltd
25 Marlborough Place, Brighton BN1 1UB
www.salariya.com
www.book-house.co.uk

1 3 5 7 9 8 6 4 2

A CIP catalogue record for this book is available from the British Library.

Printed and bound in China.

PB ISBN: 978-1-908973-26-9